Tea with my Teacher

by Kayla Johnson
Illustrated by Alisa Kokorovic and Kasia Kelly

ONION RIVER

PRESS

Onion River Press
191 Bank Street
Burlington, VT 05401

ISBN: 978-1-957184-13-5

For my family, who has always encouraged and supported me. For my daughters, may they know that they can dream big too! In celebration of my students and their families who I have always admired and loved.

A special day it will be for me.
My teacher is coming to my house for tea.
Today we need to clean and shop.
After shopping, we will mop.

Ama and I prepare the tray.
What a delightful little array!

Here she comes down the sidewalk.
Suddenly we are afraid to talk.
What if our words come out a mess?
What if bhai's sticky fingers get on her dress?

She rings the bell and takes off her shoes.
She knows all the right things to do.

She helps my parents fill out school forms,
And sits with me on the floor.

We drink strong tea from our best cups,
And eat the spicy noodles all up.

I am sad when it is time for her to go.
This visit was the best I have ever known.
This visit has made our relationship stronger,
My family and culture invisible no longer.

Kayla Johnson is a wife, mother, and educator who lives in Essex, Vermont. She loves spending time with her family, gardening, and canoeing. This is her first picture book, which was born out of a desire to have the life and culture of her students represented in literature.

Alisa Kokorovic is a senior attending Essex High School and is enrolled in the Design and Creative Media program at the Center For Technology, Essex. This is her first children's book illustration. Next year Kokorovic will be attending Champlain College for Graphic Design and Visual Communications.

Kasia Kelly is a junior at Mount Mansfield Union Highschool and is enrolled in the Design and Creative Media program at the Center For Technology, Essex. Kelly assisted with the illustrations and coloring of the children's book. Kelly will continue to attend the Design and Creative Media program next year and plans to major in Graphic Design at a college upon graduation.

Glossary

Ama- the Nepali word for mother
Bhai- the Nepali word for brother

 This is the statue of Lord Krishna, who is the god of love. It is also a symbol of luxury, beauty, and happiness in life.

 The marigold is the symbol of positive emotions and energy. Marigolds are a popular flower used to celebrate Diwali (the festival of lights). When Marigolds are grown outside, they are meant to be welcoming.

 In traditional Nepali homes, shoes and slippers are left outside. This keeps the home clean and free from bacteria. Feet are considered the dirtiest part of the body.

 Many Hindu families grow plants inside as a sign of luck and prosperity.

CPSIA information can be obtained
at www.ICGtesting.com
Printed in the USA
BVHW060043240822
645288BV00002B/19